SIENA

BUILD YOUR OWN
HUMAN SKELETON

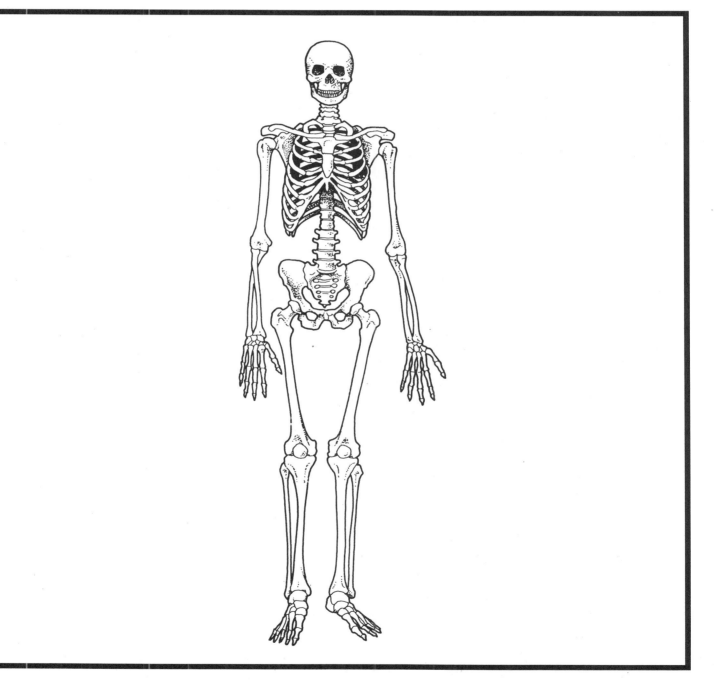

Model engineering by Pat Doyle
Colour artwork by Inkwell Studios
Other illustrations by David Woodroffe
Text by Karen Farrington and Nick Constable

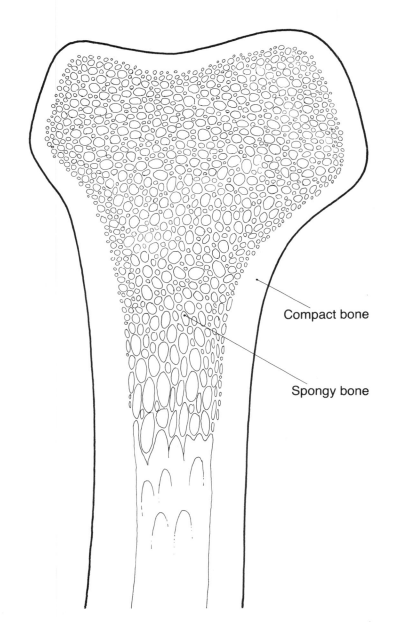

The human body is more complex than any machine or computer ever made, but without the skeleton it would fall into a blubbery mass on the floor unable to walk or talk. The skeleton is the frame that supports and protects various vital organs and tissues inside our bodies which keep us alive, including the heart and lungs.

In all there are 206 separate bones in an adult body, about three quarters of the amount we were born with. There are many more bones inside the skin of young babies, about 300 in all, but some of them gradually fuse together as the body grows.

Some bones are near the surface of your skin, like knuckles. Clench your fist and the knobbly ends of joints are clearly visible. But the thigh bone and upper-arm bone are hidden from view beneath layers of muscles and fat.

WHAT ARE BONES MADE OF?

Look in any museum and you will come away thinking bones are dry and dead. In reality, they are just the opposite. Believe it or not, bones are made up of one third to one half water.

The outer layer of the bone is called the periosteum, and it is here that broken bones are repaired. Underneath is the hard layer full of tough calcium salts, called compact bone. Here is the strength that we normally associate with bones and it comes from two natural substances, calcium carbonate and calcium phosphate. They become bone when they combine with the protein collagen. That substance protects the spongy inner bone which is full of holes.

In the shaft of some larger bones is soft marrow, threaded with blood vessels. Blood cells are made in here, as many as five billion red ones in just 24 hours. These keep us alive by delivering essential oxygen throughout the body. Some white cells are also produced, vital for fighting off invading germs. Thanks to the marrow and the spongy section, bones are not only tough but they are light as well.

So far from being dead, bones are active and bursting with life. Only the hard layer is left by the time the bone reaches a museum, and this can endure for thousands of years.

A skull of one of earth's first upright men was found in Java, Indonesia in 1891; it was an incredible 750,000 years old. Bones of animals have been found which are much older. Dinosaur bones dating back 135 million years have been discovered. Bones are preserved when they are encased in earth or mud. Then they are transformed into stone and form fossils. Always keep an eye open for fossils on the beach, where you may find the remains of a long-dead sea creature embedded in stone.

Compact bone

Spongy bone

TEETH

Inserted into the jaw of a skull are the teeth. An adult human has 32 teeth, while children have 20 first teeth, known as 'milk' teeth which fall out to be replaced by a secondary set at around the age of six. Teeth are different shapes to cope with different jobs. The molars at the back have flat tops for chewing, the front teeth are pointed to tear and cut into food.

Tooth enamel, the white, hard, outer layer, is the toughest substance in the body. It is harder even than the outer casing of bones. Below the enamel is dentine which protects the soft nerves and blood vessels growing up from the root of the tooth. The part of the tooth you can see above the gum is called the crown and it is expected to chomp its way through about half a ton of food every year.

SKULL

No fewer than 29 bones make up the human skull. Eight of them are in the cranium, the rounded shell which protects the brain. They are all slotted together through zig-zag joints which will fade and disappear by the time we have reached 40 years old.

As babies, these bones are still soft and separate. That's because the head is squeezed during birth as it leaves the mother's birth canal and needs extra flexibility. A 'soft spot' or fontanelle on top of babies' heads is visible for up to a year before the bone grows over it to make the cranium complete.

A man's brain is about 10 per cent larger than a woman's and weighs in at between 1-2 kg (2-4$^{1}/_{2}$ lb). But, of course, brain size and intelligence are not linked!

The only bone in the skull which moves is the lower jaw bone, used for chewing and talking. The eyes are protected by deep recesses in the skull, and just below the eyes there is a clearly visible hole through which some of the nerves from teeth reach up to the brain.

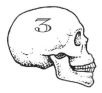

THE BACKBONE

Watch anyone stretch or touch their toes and the bumpy backbone is easy to spot. From neck to 'tail' there are 33 bones in the backbone, otherwise known as the spine. These bones are called vertebrae. All of them are linked with joints and some of them are fused together to make a distinctive S-shape. The backbone is strong yet supple. This is because discs of cartilage separate each bone, giving the backbone flexibility, like the cord of a shower, for example. However, during the day as you walk around the discs are squashed down, while at night when you sleep they relax. This means you are taller when you wake up in the morning than when you go to bed at night.

The function of the vertebrae is to protect the spinal cord, the major nerve that links the brain to the rest of the body. If the spinal cord is out of action, our brain would not be able to tell our bodies to walk, throw, run or catch. Although we would still be able to breathe and digest food with a damaged spinal cord, our physical abilities would be severely impaired.

Not all animals have backbones. Among those without are worms, jellyfish or insects. They are called invertebrates. Some animals don't have an internal skeleton but carry a protective hard casing on the outside of their bodies. This suit of armour is called 'exoskeleton'. Unlike human bones, it does not expand and grow. Animals with exoskeletons, like beetles and shellfish, must shed it when it gets too small and make a larger one. Turtles and tortoises have both internal skeletons and an exoskeleton which grow together until they become joined. The shell protects them like steel plating but hampers their speed and progress.

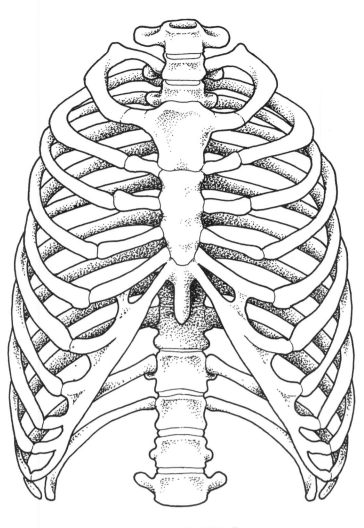

THE RIBS

Sprouting out of the backbone, from just below the neck to just above the waist, are the ribs. They curve around and most join the breast bone or sternum at the front of the body, providing a cage which protects the heart, lungs and some important blood vessels.

The two pairs of ribs at the bottom of the cage do not join the breast bone. These are called floating ribs.

The normal quota of ribs is 12 pairs. Not everyone has this many though. Some have 11 or 13 pairs. There is no explanation for this and it doesn't do any harm.

Breath in and out deeply and you will feel your rib cage moving. The heavily muscled heart uses its regular beat to pump blood around the body. In humans it is found on the left hand side of the chest cavity. When the rib cage is thrust out, it increases the capacity of the lungs and air rushes in.

So the rib cage helps us to breathe too.

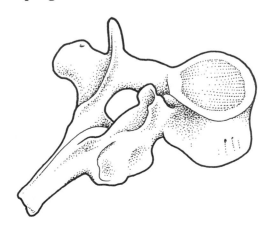

HOW BONES ARE JOINED

Although bones are rigid the skeleton moves with ease because of joints, ligaments and cartilage, which connect one bone to another. We rely on these for agility and comfort.

Short, tough strips of tissue joining one bone to another are called ligaments. At the bone end is cartilage from which all bones develop. Children and babies have a lot of cartilage which slowly turns into bone as they grow.

However, there is cartilage in the joints which never hardens off, as it does in the rest of the bone. It provides a cushion which allows one bone to operate independently in close proximity to the next. There's synovial fluid surrounding the joint which is kept in place by a membrane. Without this fluid which oils or lubricates the joint, our bones would grind against each other. There are more than 200 joints in our bodies, almost one for every bone.

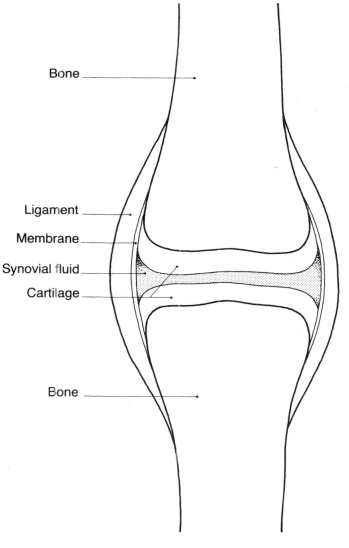

Bone

Ligament

Membrane

Synovial fluid

Cartilage

Bone

BONES AND MUSCLES

All of us have muscles, not just the people who play sports. We have about 650, to be precise. Muscles enable us to move and make expressions on our faces. Smiling uses 17 muscles but a frown needs 43.

If you want to feel some muscles in your face at work, put your fingertips on your head each side of your eyes and talk.

Those found just under our skins are called voluntary muscles, that is, they do what our brain tells them to do. Each one is a collection of long, narrow cells known as fibres, bundled together and housed in a membrane. Among the fibres are tiny blood capillaries and nerves. It is the nerves which carry signals from the brain to the muscles, telling them where and how to move. A tendon anchors the muscles to the bones of the skeleton. When the muscle contracts or gets shorter, it pulls the bone and makes it move. Some muscles work in pairs like those in the upper arm. To raise the lower arm the biceps muscle in the upper arm shortens and the triceps muscle is relaxed. To lower the arm the process is put into reverse. Muscles which bend a limb at a joint are called flexors. Muscles which straighten the limb are known as extensors. The web of muscles which cover your body and work together with the skeleton can pull but are unable to push.

Muscles are heavy and make up between a third and a half of our body weight. The biggest are in our legs, buttocks and arms. The smallest muscle is in our ear, measuring just one millimetre. Still more muscles exist in the digestive system, lungs, eyes and bladder. But we have no control over them and so they are called involuntary muscles.

Strongest of all these are the muscles that occur in our hearts known as cardiac muscles. They are made up differently to the muscles we use for movement, however. In them fibres are crossed and branched instead of being in tidy bundles.

Most muscles in the body are mirrored to make a pair. For example, a muscle in the left arm has a corresponding partner in the right arm. They are not only attached to the bone but also the skin and in some cases, to each other, to give extra strength. Muscles may be flat, ribbon-

5

shaped, spread out like a fan or in a twist.

Muscles in the cheek help us to bite and chew. Another set of muscles extends from the temples, between your eyes and your ears, to give added power. Clench your teeth hard and see if you can feel it in action.

THE PIVOT JOINT

The head sits on top of the backbone on a pivot joint. It looks like a ring fitting snugly on to a peg. With this joint you can move your head up and down and from side to side.

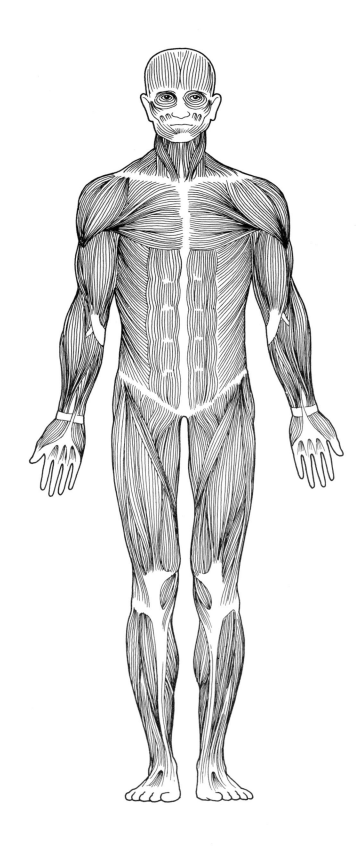

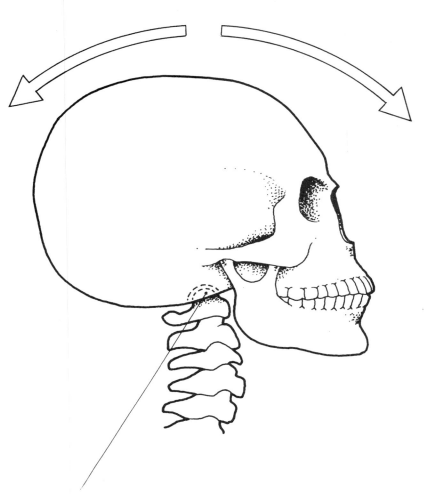

Pivot joint

THE SADDLE JOINT

Between the thumb and the hand lies the saddle joint, which is especially important as it allows us to pick up things easily. We need our hands for all kinds of activities. That's why there are more than 50 bones in the hands alone – almost a quarter of the body's total. Without our agile thumb, the scope for movement in our hands would be very basic.

THE BALL AND SOCKET JOINT

There's a ball on the top of the leg joint which fits into a socket on the pelvis or hip bone. Accordingly, you can move your thigh and legs in all directions, like the joy stick on a computer. It gives more freedom of movement than any other joint in the body.

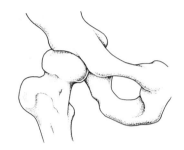

THE HINGE JOINT

All fingers have hinge joints but the best example is perhaps that of the elbow or the knee. The hinge allows movement in one direction only, just like the hinge of a door.

Hinge joint

Saddle joint

Condyloid joint

THE CONDYLOID JOINT

It's much simpler to remember it as the wrist which, thanks to this joint, can rotate usefully. The hand bones come together in a dome shape which rests in a corresponding curve at the bottom of the arm bones. Shake your hands about and you will see they move forwards and backwards a long way and just a little way side to side.

MAKING THE SKELETON

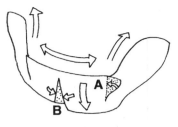

PLEASE NOTE THAT LEFT AND RIGHT OF THE SKELETON ARE AS VIEWED FROM THE FRONT.

You will need an ordinary craft knife with renewable blades, a small pair of scissors and an ordinary ballpoint pen that has run out of ink. Use a small tube of contact adhesive glue (the sort that goes onto each surface to be stuck and is then left to dry for a few moments before the parts are pressed together).

Work in a well-lit area where you can leave your model parts without them being damaged. Use a plastic cutting board or a thick sheet of cardboard to protect the furniture.

Remove the model pages from the book before cutting them to shape. Read the instructions and look at the drawings to ensure you understand the assembly stages before starting to cut the parts. If you are not sure go back over the instructions.

Only cut the parts as you need them in assembly. Cut along the solid black lines, pressing just enough to cut through the card. Cut slowly.

Crease the dotted lines with the ballpoint pen by running it along the line gently to make a mark and then going over it again to make a deeper crease. Try this on a piece of scrap card first to see how it works.

Do not apply glue straight from the tube. Use a strip of thick card like a narrow brush to spread the glue exactly where it is needed on the hatched areas. Use these areas to position the parts.

Line up the parts before pressing them into place. Take your time, don't rush, and check every step first.

Work with the skeleton flat. Finally, hang the finished model from its hanger in the back of the skull.

Go over the complete model and squeeze all the arm and leg bones to an even shape. Arms can be bent in or out, across the chest, etc.

STEP 3

Cut out and shape jaw as arrowed. Glue at A and B.

STEP 4

Assemble the three sections together as shown.
Line up top edge of face to skull at A, and glue.
Line up B and C to back of face sides and glue.
Leave a 3-5mm gap between jaw and face and glue at D.

Shape curve, then glue all into Skull Former.
Fold out the hanger tap so the top of the spine can be glued in here. Finally, squeeze sides and cheek curves to complete the skull.

STEP 5

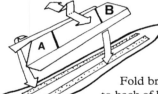

Cut out Breast Bone Brace, Breast Bone, Chest Spacer and the two halves of the Spine. Cut the two slots A and B.
Fold breast bone brace to shape and glue to back of breast bone exactly central, side to side and end to end as shown.

STEP 6

Glue spine halves together at B and to back of skull below hanger tab at A.
Fold and glue the chest spacer to box shape.
Pass tabs through spine from the front and fold over flat at C. Do not glue the spacer into place.

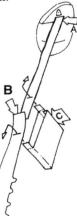

STEP 1

Cut out and curve the top of the skull. Bring together and glue A, B and C. Make sure the surface is even.

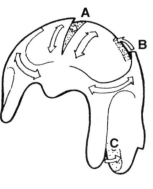

STEP 2

Cut out and curve face.
Bring top edges together and glue at A.
Cut out and shape nose and glue into nose opening (from behind).
Cut out and glue cheeks B to either side of the face at C folding the flaps right back.

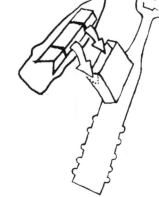

STEP 7

Turn spine assembly over, face up, and put breast bone assembly into the chest spacer so that cuts drop over ends of chest spacer, as shown.

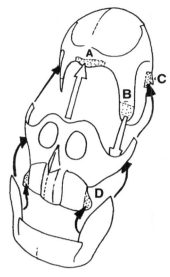

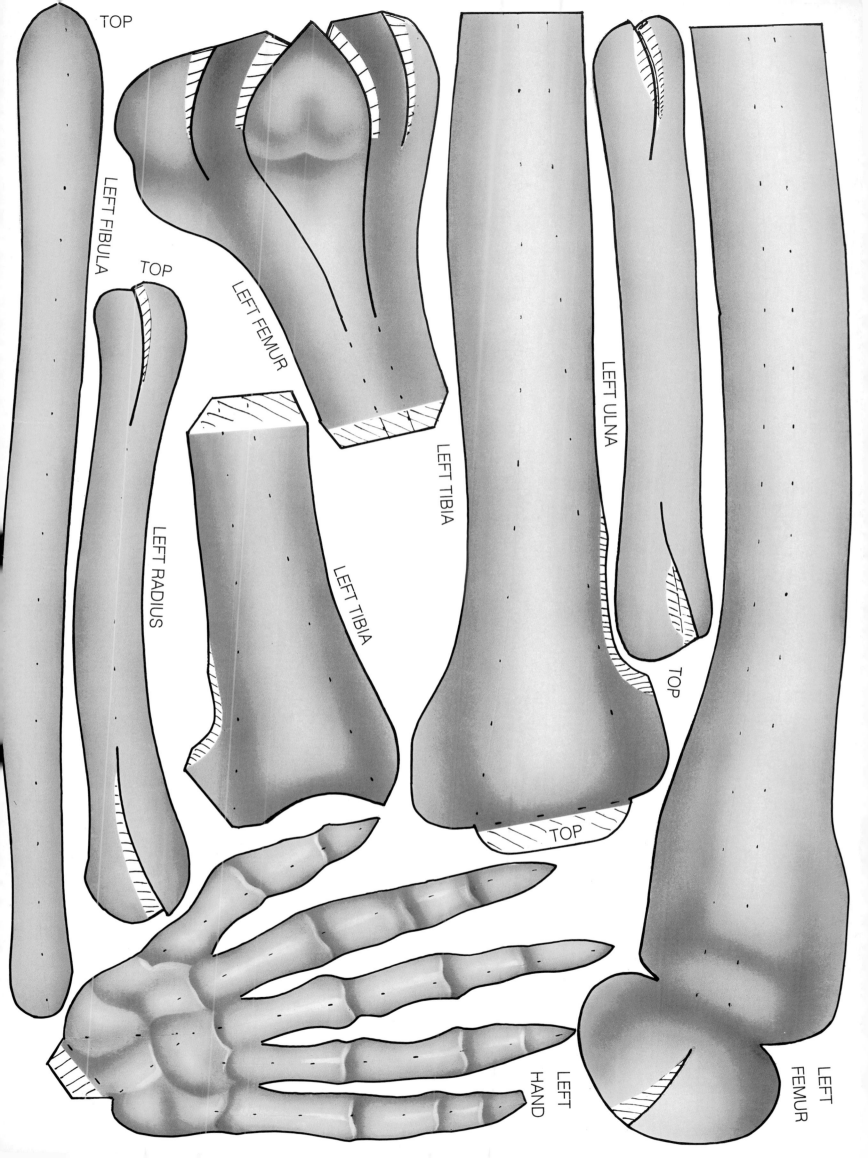

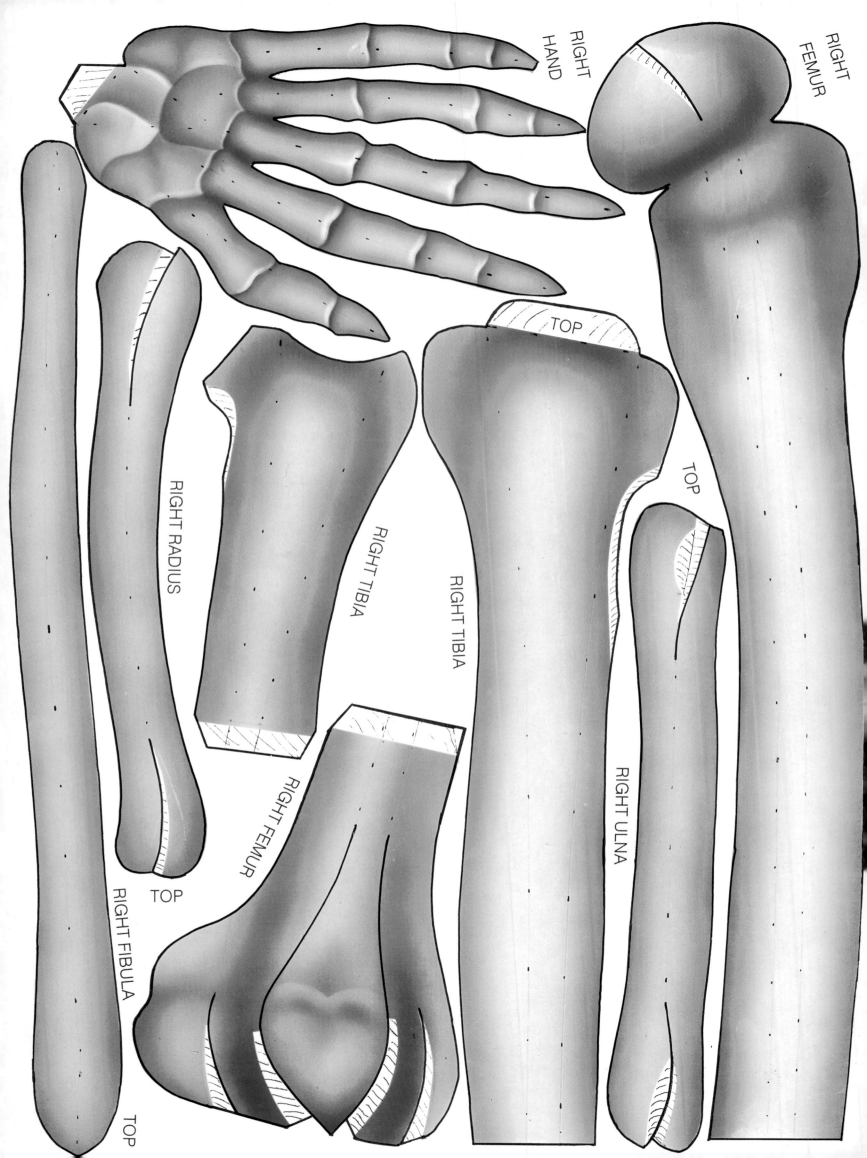

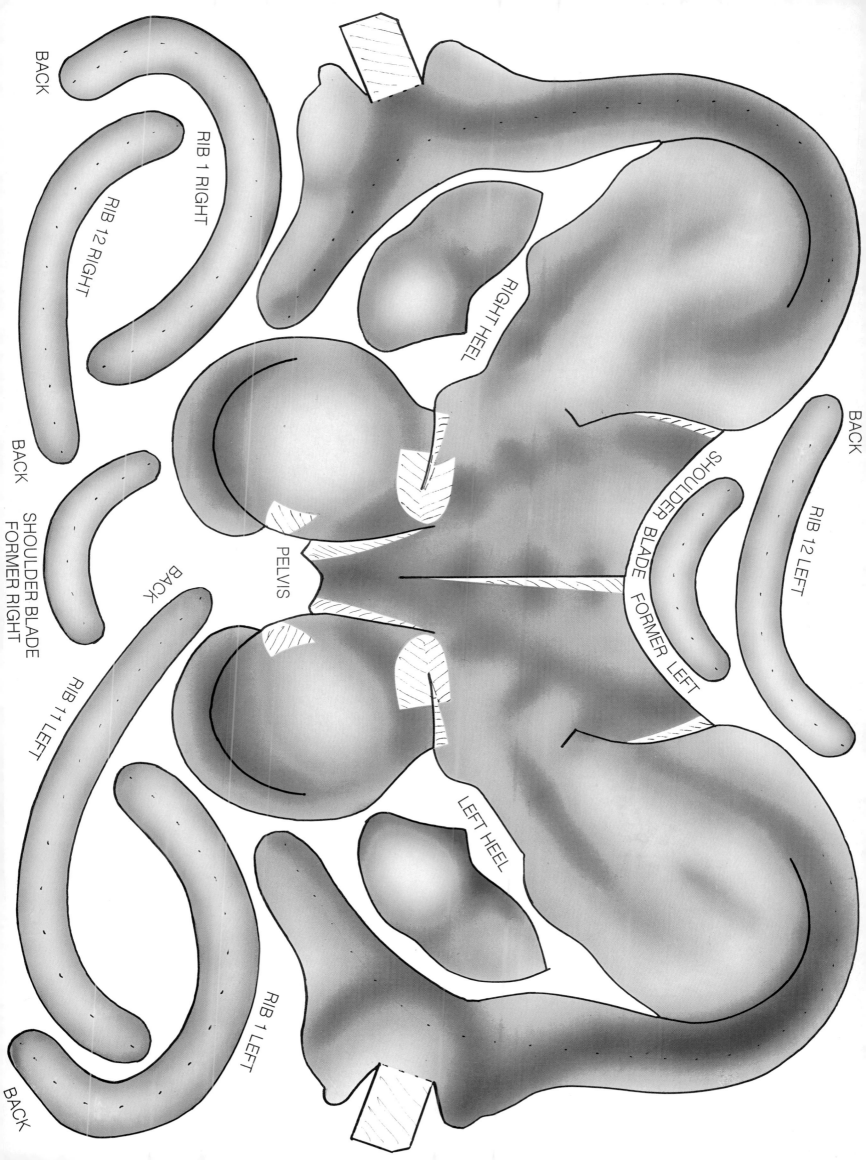

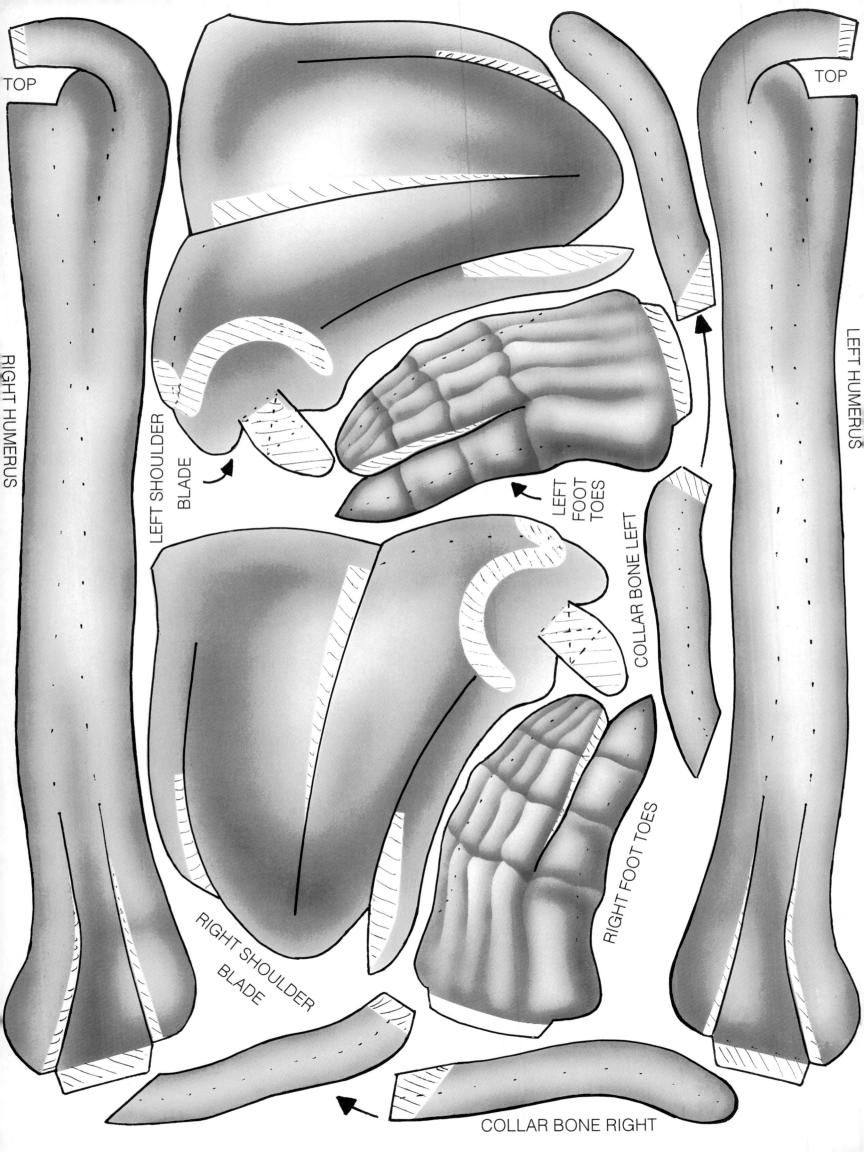

TOP

TOP

RIGHT HUMERUS

LEFT HUMERUS

LEFT SHOULDER BLADE

LEFT FOOT TOES

COLLAR BONE LEFT

RIGHT SHOULDER BLADE

RIGHT FOOT TOES

COLLAR BONE RIGHT

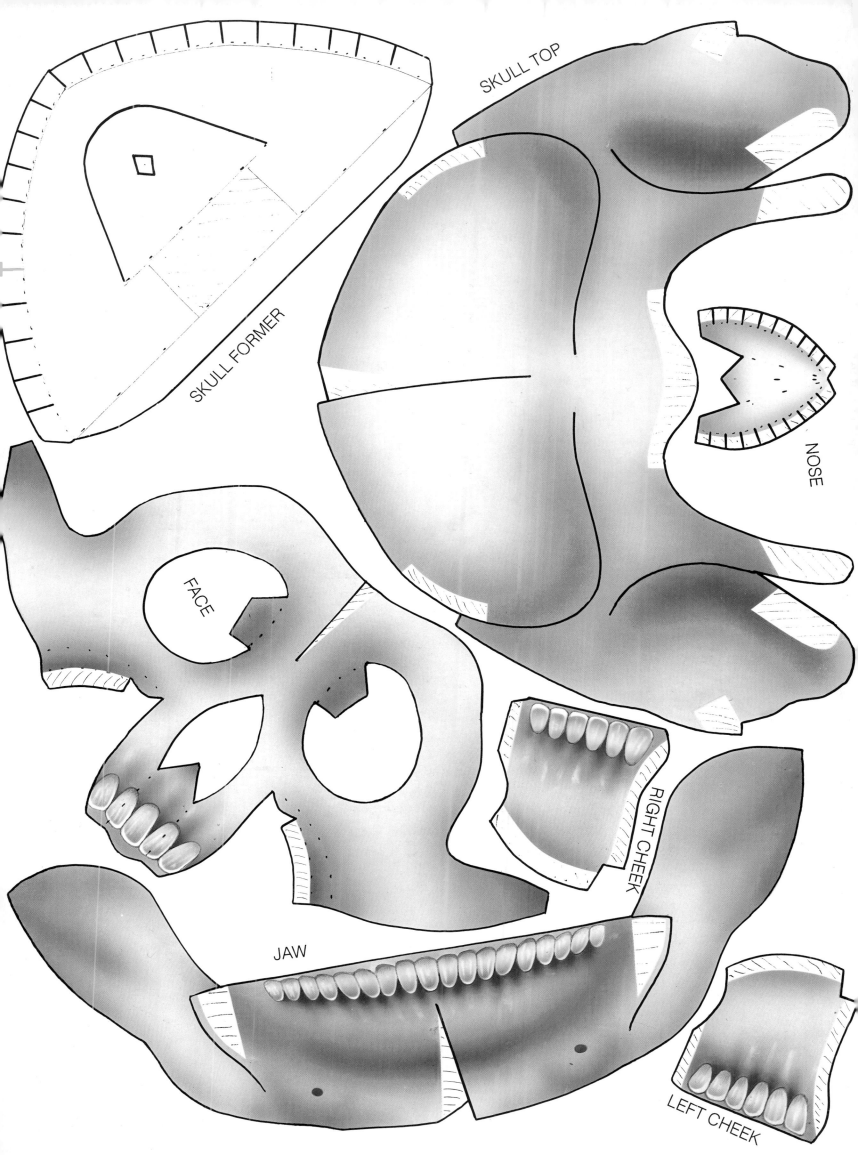

SKULL FORMER

SKULL TOP

NOSE

FACE

RIGHT CHEEK

JAW

LEFT CHEEK

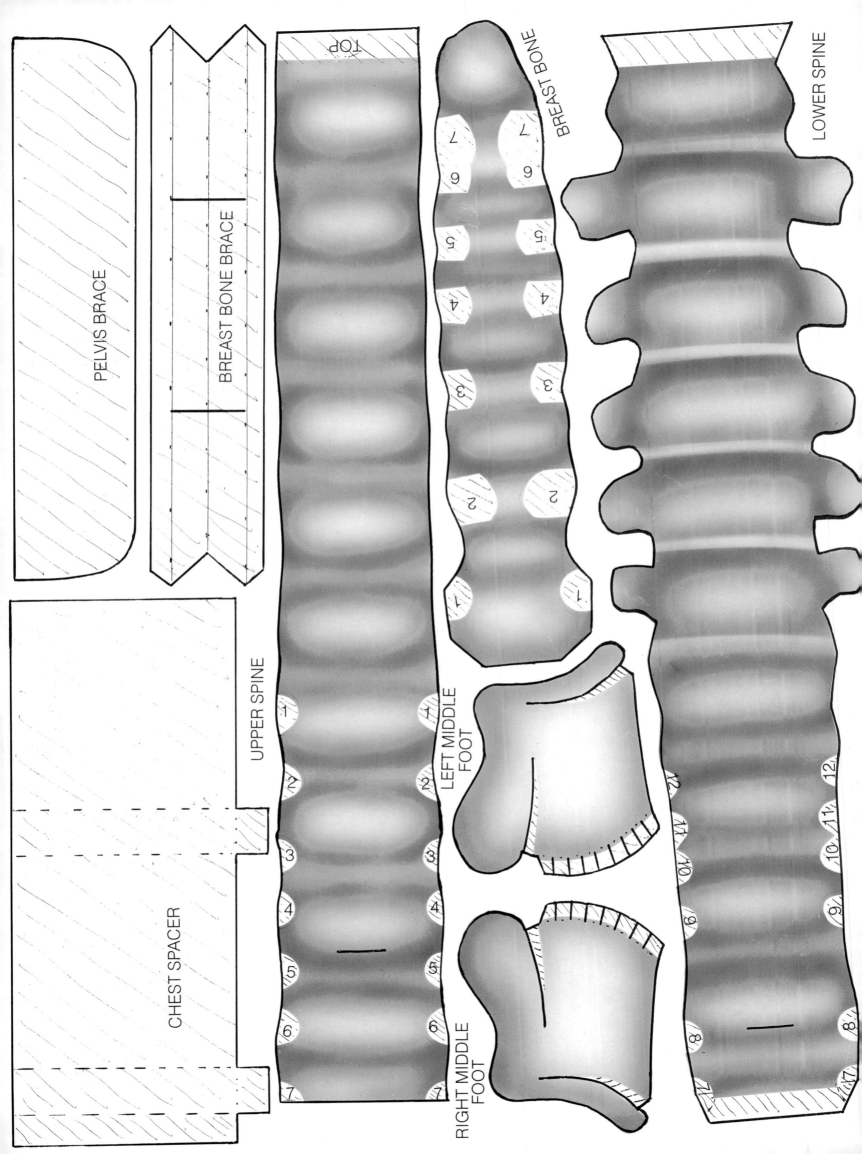

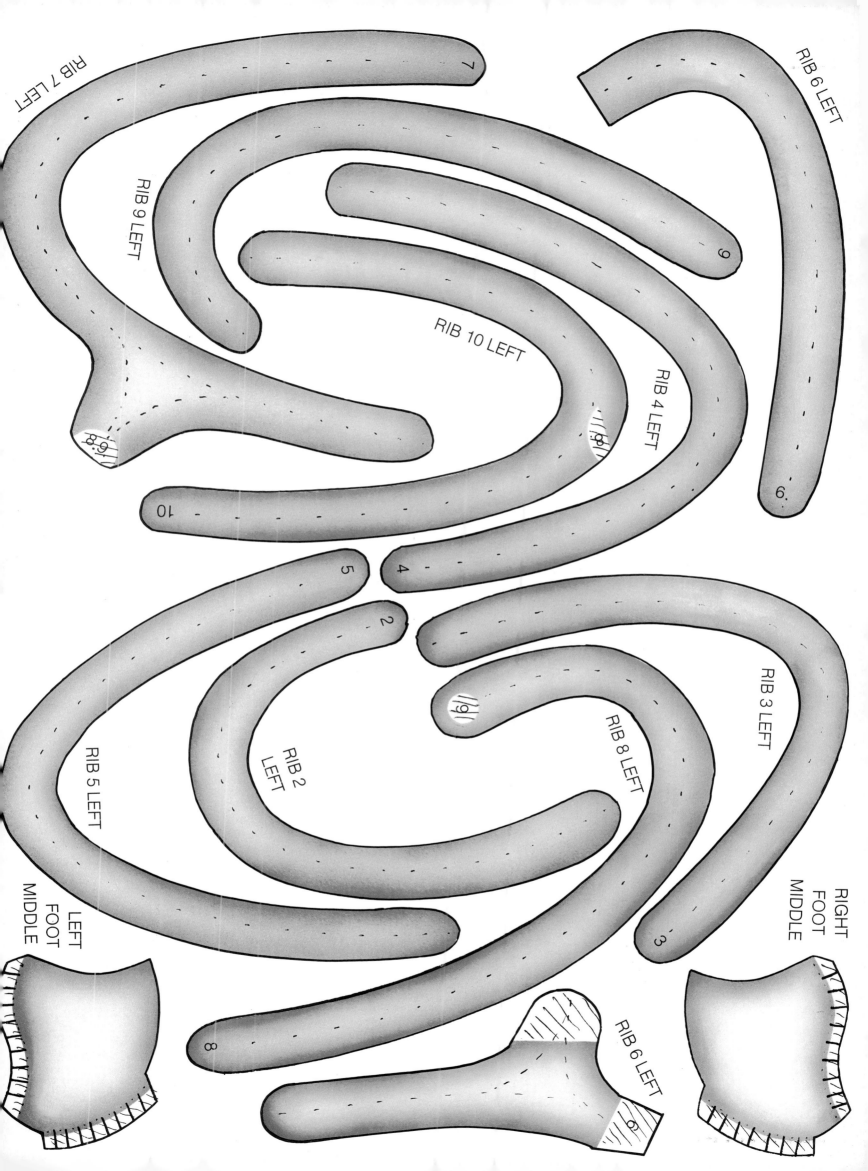

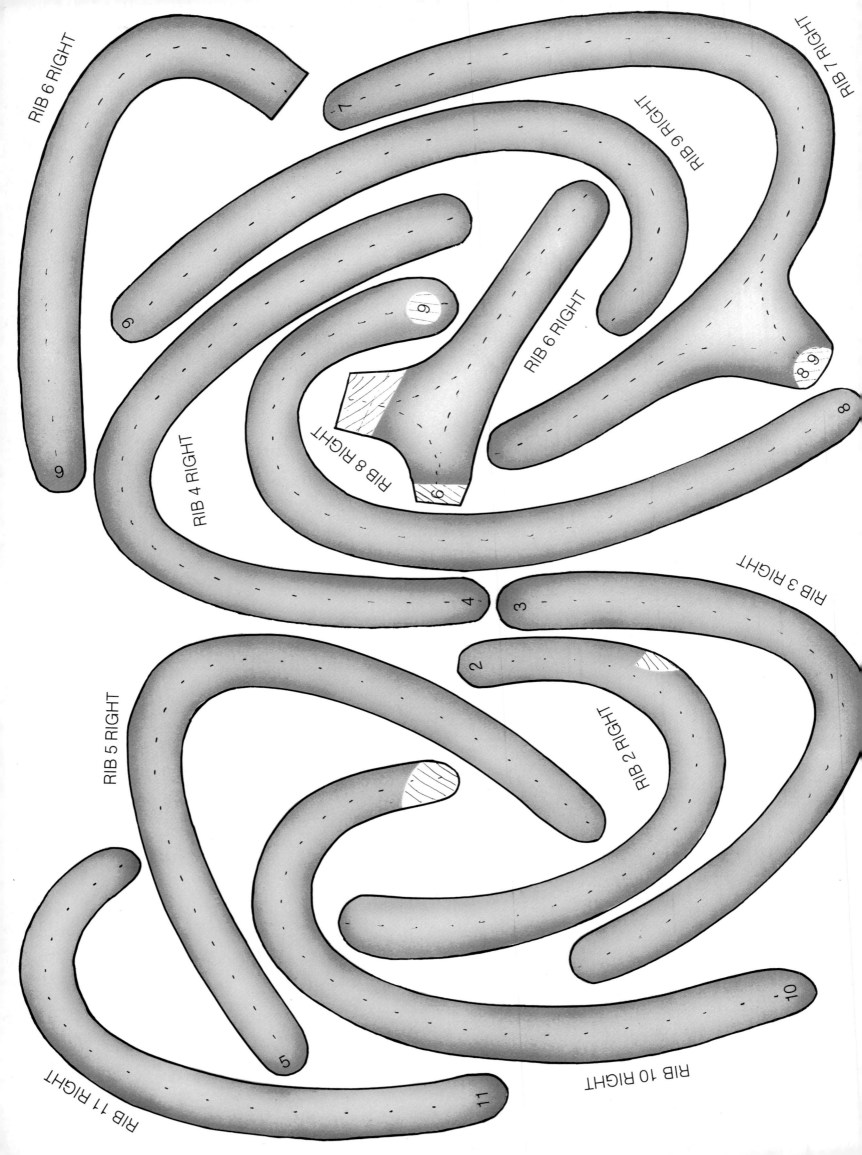

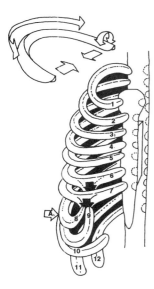

STEP 8

Cut out ribs. They are numbered, 1 to 7 glue to the breast bone.
Crease ribs along the dotted lines and curve them inward, into a V shape, as shown.
Glue the ribs in pairs. Ensure they are evenly positioned and that the breast bone remains central to the skeleton and upright.
Make up ribs 6 and glue to the back edge of 7. Ribs 8 and 9 glue to the centre tip of 7.
Rib 10 glues to the outer edge of 8 at A.
Ribs 11 and 12 glue to spine like the others but are shaped and positioned as shown.

Tear off 2 rear tabs on chest spacer and REMOVE by slightly raising the rib cage.

NOTE:
Rib positions are marked on the spine and the breast bone.

STEP 9

Cut out shoulders and shoulder blade formers. Glue together shoulders, shaping into forward curve as you go.
Crease shoulder blade formers as ribs and glue into position as shown.
Cut out, crease and curve collar bones, as ribs.

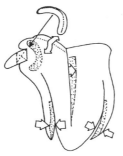

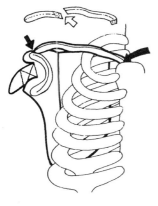

STEP 10

Glue upper right corner of left shoulder blade to upper edge of rib 2, 15mm to the left of the spine and position as shown.
Curve lower edge of shoulder blade in and glue to the nearest rib. Maintain the position as shown.
Repeat for right shoulder blade.
Glue left and right collar bones to shoulder blades and breast bone as shown.

STEP 11

Cut out and glue areas on front of pelvis, curving to shape.
Curve side strips

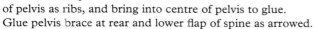

of pelvis as ribs, and bring into centre of pelvis to glue.
Glue pelvis brace at rear and lower flap of spine as arrowed.

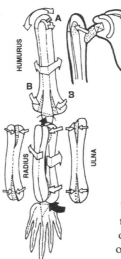

STEP 12

Cut out all the left arm and hand bones.
Fold long creases on humerus to shape, curve top strip and glue at A. Bring lower strips together and glue at B.
Fold centre creases of ulna and radius. Bring together and glue; make sure you know the top of each bone.
Glue radius onto the ulna and then both into position at the bottom of the humerus; then bend all creases on the hand and glue to the bottom of the ulna and radius. Finally, glue completed arm to the left of the skeleton and glue left shoulder blade tab into top rear of the completed arm.

STEP 13

Cut out all left leg bones.
Bend creases in upper and lower femur and glue the two halves

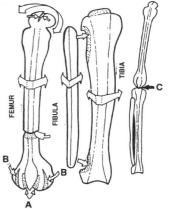

together. Curve top of femur and glue as arrowed. Bring lower flaps together and glue at A and B.
Bend creases in fibula and tibia to shape and glue fibula in position on tibia as arrowed.
Glue halves of leg together at knee joint as arrowed C.

STEP 14

Cut out all left foot bones.
Curve parts of foot and glue together.
Bring front of toes together and glue.
Glue flaps on centre foot as shown. Glue rear of foot in position.
Glue heel in place under rounded flap of centre foot and along curved flap at rear of foot.
Glue foot to leg.

STEP 15

Glue legs to small creased flaps on pelvis. Glue flaps into back of femur with rounded top level with crease arrowed A.

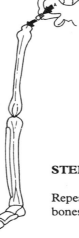

STEP 16

Repeat steps 12-15 using all the right hand side bones. Your skeleton is now complete.

SKIN

This elastic layer of cells, called skin, does marvellous work covering muscles and bones. It keeps in heat when you are cold and allows it to escape when things heat up. It keeps germs at bay, heals quickly, gives you the sense of touch and helps to grow hair and nails.

Skin is made up of cells. But the skin you can see when you look at yourself is all dead. Living cells are protected by this outer layer called the epidermis. The skin makes new cells at the same time as shedding old ones. A new cell is made when an existing one swells and stretches until it divides into two. It takes about 28 days for a skin cell to live, thrive and then die.

The skin is thinnest on the eyelids and lips, measuring only about 0.5 millimetres (.039 in). But on the soles of your feet the skin is much thicker, about 3 millimetres (.23 in).

Look at the tips of your fingers. Each one bears a swirling pattern of minute ridges. This pattern on your skin was formed before you were born and is unique to you. That's why police investigators place so much importance on fingerprints left at the scene of a crime. With special dust they can find the pattern belonging to people who have been in the vicinity and trace their identity. To get a closer look at your fingerprint, press the tip of your finger onto an ink pad and make a print on a plain white piece of paper. Compare it to a friend's.

BONE MEALS

Like the rest of our body, bones need food to flourish and grow. The best foods for bones are those which contain Vitamins C and D and some minerals. They are not only good for bones but help teeth grow strong too.

THE EAR

Three tiny bones in your ear make the difference between a world of silence and a blast of sound. Beyond your ear flap is a canal which leads to the ear drum. Sounds travelling through this canal make the drum vibrate. In turn the vibrations are passed on by the trio of all important bones, the hammer, anvil and stirrup, collectively known as the ear ossicles. After the ossicles comes the cochlea, a chamber filled with fluid. Movement inside the fluid triggers tiny hairs. The nerve endings at the base of the hairs put the auditory nerve in motion and the sound is translated to the brain. Even though it sounds very complicated, the hearing process happens very quickly – but there is a delay between the instant the sound is made and the moment it is registered by the brain. You will see a roaring jet in the sky before you hear the noise of its engines. The gap is so slight you might not even notice. But it is there.

Ears are not only important for listening and hearing sounds. They also help you keep your balance. The liquid in the ear stays level, no matter whether you are standing upright or lying on your side. As it reaches its level, nerves in the liquid tell the brain what is happening and it can send out messages to the limbs which will help co-ordination.

The liquid also makes you feel dizzy after you have been spinning. For even after you have stopped turning, the liquid keeps going. So even if you are standing still, your brain believes you are still on the move and your body feels mixed up.

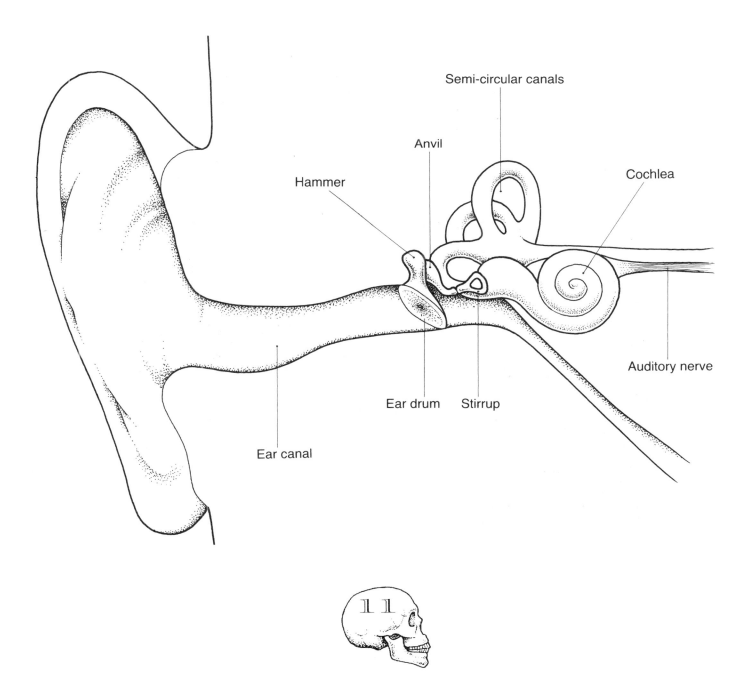

Semi-circular canals

Anvil

Hammer

Cochlea

Ear drum   Stirrup

Auditory nerve

Ear canal

11

INJURING YOUR BONES

When bones break they are fractured. Anyone with a fracture must see a doctor at hospital who will set it in plaster.

Plaster sets hard around the injury, forcing the broken ends of the bone back together again until they can heal naturally. The bone itself will first bridge the crack created by a break with a fibrous material. Then bone-making cells get to work and soon it's complete again.

Some bones broken in several places may need extra help. That's when doctors turn to their 'tool kit' and use screws and plates to join the shattered bone while it heals.

If doctors want to take a closer look at the injury or make sure it is properly healed, they will organise an X-ray for you. This is a way of photographing what is under the skin. Each bone looks lit up thanks to the X-ray machine which was first invented a century ago, in 1895, by German physicist W. C. Roentgen.

Sometimes children who stumble and land awkwardly suffer a sprain. That happens when the ligaments holding a joint together are damaged. It's painful and usually the injured joint will swell. If cold bandages and a long rest don't cure the injury, it is important to see a doctor.

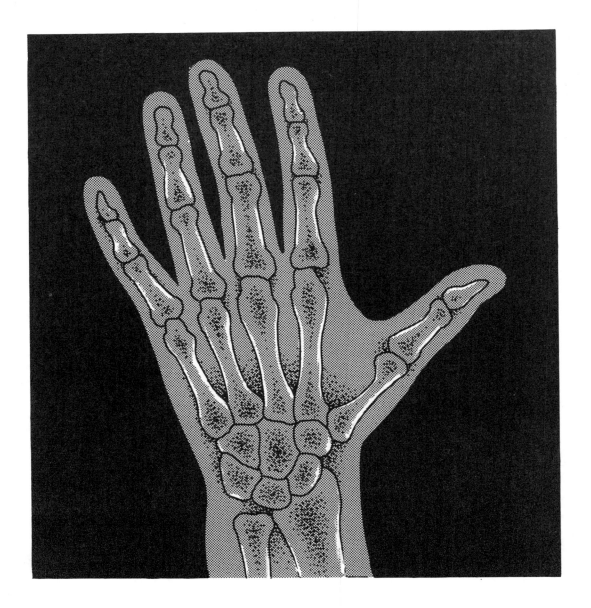

12

PAINT YOUR FACE

Although you can never see your own bones, except in an X-ray, you can use face paints to make your face look like a skull or a skeleton. This is a great idea for Halloween or fancy dress.

The best paints are water-based and to apply them, make sure you have some sponges and a couple of brushes, one thick and one thin. Before you start, put on an apron to protect your clothes.

Check to make sure your skin will not have an allergic reaction to the paint by putting a spot of paint on the back of your hand and waiting for a few hours to make sure the skin does not become red, itchy or painful.

TO DRAW A SKULL

When you are ready to begin, sponge in a base of white paint all over your face, up to the beginning of your hair and down to your neck. With a dry sponge, dab a little green colour around the edges and to make it look creepier, and use grey under your cheek bones to resemble the hollows of a skull.

With a paint brush paint a circle around your eyes with black paint and fill it in, so the eyelids are black as well. Then paint two triangles each side of the nose and mouth, pointing towards your nostrils. It will make the skin look hollow.

Still with black paint, and with your lips closed, paint a big rectangle around your mouth and then draw lines from the top of it to the bottom, leaving spaces to look like white lumpy teeth.

To finish paint jagged cracks in black on your forehead. If you paint white lines alongside them, they will look as if they run really deep.

Now, cover your hair and neck with a black cloth or scarf to complete the effect.

TO DRAW A SKELETON

You can also paint your face with a whole skeleton. Copying from the picture on page 1 of this book, use white paint to put a skull on your forehead. Draw shoulders, arms and hands above your eyebrows and around by your ears.

Put the backbone and the rib cage down the nose and complete it with the pelvis at the end on the beginning of your cheeks. Your nostrils will then appear to be the hole which exists in the hip bone.

The thighs come next, along the creases between the nose and the mouth. Paint the shins and feet dangling from the corners of your mouth. Use a paintbrush with black to outline the skeleton.

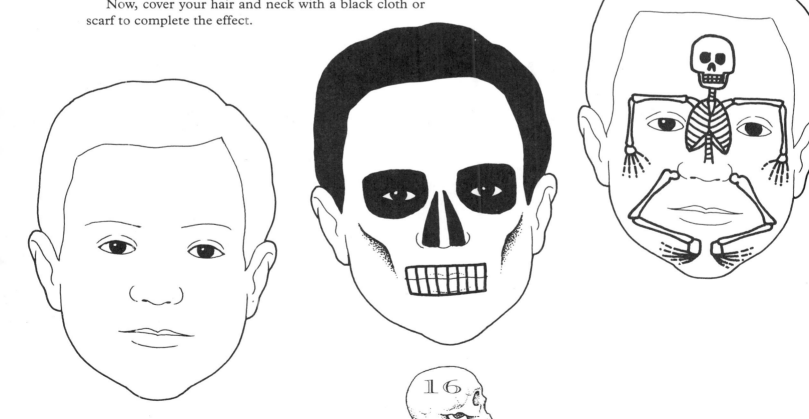

16

A Siena book. Siena is an imprint of Parragon Books. First published in Great Britain in 1994 by Parragon Book Service, Units 13–17, Avonbridge Trading Estate, Atlantic Road, Avonmouth, Bristol, BS11 9QD. © Parragon Book Service Ltd, 1994. Printed in Great Britain. This edition reprinted 1996. ISBN 1 85813 463 3.

WORDSEARCH

There are 10 words linked to the human skeleton hidden in the box of letters below. All words are in a straight line but may read backwards or forwards, up or down, or diagonally. You may use letters twice.

```
O  L  F  T  M  C  C  S
S  C  R  A  N  I  U  M
S  M  A  E  R  U  U  A
I  T  C  L  C  B  I  R
C  S  T  B  C  J  A  R
L  I  U  O  A  I  W  O
E  R  R  W  O  B  U  W
S  W  E  C  E  L  L  M
```

The hidden words are: Cranium, Ossicles, Jaw, Elbow, Marrow, Cell, Rib, Fracture, Wrist, Calcium.

MUSCULOSKELETAL SYSTEM

This is the word for bones, muscles and joints all pulling together to make your body work. See how many words of three letters or more you can make out of these two words. Remember, you can use any combination of letters but don't use the same letter twice in one word. Plurals don't count. There are at least seven different animals hidden in it as well as three words connected to the body – and many more.

A – Z OF BODY LANGUAGE

As we have seen, the skeleton is unable to work in isolation.
It needs muscles, the skin, organs and blood to shape it into the human form we recognise when we look in the mirror. Here are a few words to give you top-to-toe knowledge of your body.

A – Antibody, a white cell made by the blood to fight germs.

B – Bladder, a stretchy sack which collects waste water.

C – Cell, tiny particles which make up all living things.

D – Diaphragm, a sheet of muscle below the lungs which helps you breathe.

E – Elastin, a rubbery material which reinforces tendons.

F – Follicle, the hole which houses the root of a hair.

G – Gall bladder, which stores bile, a juice for digestion.

H – Hormones, chemical messengers which control the body's growth.

I – Intestines, tubes in which food is broken down.

J – Joint, the junction between bones that allows movement.

K – Keratin, a hard substance that makes hair, nails and skin.

L – Larynx, the part of your windpipe that contains the vocal cords.

M – Musculoskeletal System, the combination of bones, muscles and joints.

N – Nerves, message lines from the brain.

O – Oesophagus, the food pipe.

P – Palatine bone, found in the roof of the mouth.

Q – Quinsy, acute sore throat.

R – Radiologist, the person in hospital who takes X-rays.

S – Sacrum, a single bone in the lower back made up of five fused vertebrae.

T – Tissue, a group of cells all doing the same job.

U – Urea, body waste which becomes urine.

V – Vertebrae, small bones in the back which join up to make the spine.

W – Water, a vital component of bones, so always drink plenty.

X – X-Ray, a special photograph which reveals what's under the skin.

Y – Yawn, which you do when your body needs an oxygen boost.

Z – Zygomatic bones, another name for cheekbones.

KNOW YOUR BONES

Calcaneus – heel bone

Carpals – wrist bones, eight in each hand

Cervical vertebrae – neck bones

Clavicle – collar bone

Coccyx – base of back bone

Cranium – part of skull which protects the brain

Femur – thigh bone

Fibia – one of two bones in lower leg

Frontal bone – forehead

Humerus – upper arm

Lumbar vertebrae – lower back

Mandible – lower jaw bone

Maxilla – upper jaw

Metacarpals – palm bones

Metatarsals – foot bones

Occipital bone – back of head

Patella – knee bone

Parietal bone – side of head

Pelvis – hip bone, made of six fused bones

Phalanges – fingers or toes

Radius – one of two bones in lower arm

Sacrum – backbone joined to pelvis

Scapula – shoulder blade

Sternum – breast bone running down the centre of the rib cage

Tarsal bones – bones in ankle, seven in each foot

Tibia – one of two bones in lower leg

Thoracic vertebrae – back bone behind the chest

Ulna – one of two bones in lower arm

Vertebrae – bones of the back

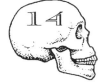

TAKE CARE

We know that bones can break through accidents. But there are other ways of damaging them too. When you stand, your spine should be curving gently, not slumped forward. So keep your chin up, your chest out, your shoulders back and you will avoid putting stresses on the backbone which could cause problems in later life.

Babies' feet are a perfect, well-sculptured shape until they begin to walk. And it is not walking that ruins their delightful toes, it is shoes. Well-fitting shoes are important, especially in childhood. Shoes which pinch will begin to mould the soft bones of the foot, causing ugly lumps and bumps. Bones don't finally harden until you are 25, so it is just as important to find

comfortable shoes which fit your feet during your teenage years as well.

When you see a new baby, it is floppy, hardly able to move its limbs. As it grows it gains more and more control of its muscles and body, first by crawling then by walking. A baby striving to walk is getting exercise to strengthen its muscles. The best way to keep muscles strong, supple and toned is to continue exercising from babyhood throughout your life for as long as you are able.

With age, bones become more brittle and take longer to heal. Some unfortunate people suffer from a disease called osteoporosis which makes their bones break easily, so it's important they do not trip over or fall down.

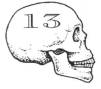

13